FAIR FIELDS

The Filipinos

Tana Reiff

ADAMS TWELVE Five Star Schools
ESL Department
Learning Services
Julie Jensen, Coordinator
(720) 972-4273

Globe
Fearon

Upper Saddle River,
New Jersey

HOPES *and* DREAMS 2

Printed in the United States of America
  4 5 6 7 8 9 10 04 03 02 01 00

Library of Congress Catalog Card Number: 92–71061

ISBN 0–8224–3808–9

Globe
Fearon

CONTENTS

1 Early Days in Hawaii

A hospital room in California, 1975
and looking back to Hawaii, 1922

"Time for your shot,"
the young nurse said
to the old man.
"Let's see your right arm."

Fabian Beltran
put out his arm
and made a fist.
"I know what to do,"
he told the nurse.

The nurse looked at
Fabian's hand and arm.
"You've done some hard work
in your day,
haven't you?"
she asked.

"Very hard work,"
said the old man.
"Starting with that sugar cane
in Hawaii.
That was way back
in the 1920s.
And I've done a lot of hard work
ever since then.
But cutting sugar cane—
that was the worst.
You young Filipinos
coming over now
have it easy.
Most of you
are nurses or doctors."

"We work hard, too,"
smiled the nurse.
She pulled the needle
back out of Fabian's arm.
"All done," she said.

"Sometime I'll tell you
about my days in Hawaii,"
said Fabian.
"And then I'll tell you

about going to California
and picking grapes.
And I'll tell you
how we were treated
and about our fight
for fair pay and a better life."

"You can start right now,"
said the nurse.
"Then you can tell me
a little of your story
every time I stop by.
I don't know much
about the early Filipinos
in America.
Being Filipino myself,
I'd like to learn more."

Fabian put his head back
and began to remember
when he first left the Philippines.
He began
to tell the nurse his story.

The sugar cane growers in Hawaii
sent people to the Philippines

to find workers.
They told the young men
that if they came to Hawaii
they wouldn't be poor anymore.
They would get good pay,
a clean place to live,
and a doctor
when they needed one.
What's more,
the growers would pay
for the trip to Hawaii.

Fabian and his friend Edmundo
couldn't pass this up.
So in 1922,
they signed papers
saying they would work
for three years.
And off they went to Hawaii.
Fabian was only 16 years old.

Once in Hawaii,
far away from home,
the young men worked
on a sugar cane plantation.
They worked six days a week,

ten hours a day.
They planted.
They worked the fields
while the cane grew.
When it was time to cut the cane,
the fields were burned black
to help make the cane
easy to cut.
But it was still hard work.
And in only a few hours,
everyone was covered with black.
When the cane was cut
the field hands loaded it onto carts
to carry it to the sugar mills.

The pay was not as high
as the man had said it would be.
Still, Fabian made enough
to send money home.

"We didn't have it easy,"
the old man told the nurse.
"But the *compang* helped."

"What's a *compang*?"
asked the nurse.

"Well, I didn't have a family
on the plantation,"
Fabian explained.
"There weren't even women.
So a group of us
made our own little family.
That's a *compang*.
The oldest man
was like the father.
We all helped each other.
We also made
a pretty good baseball team!"

"You played baseball
on the plantation?"
asked the nurse.

"We did have our fun,"
said Fabian.
"But you haven't heard
the really bad part yet."

"Tell me tomorrow,"
said the nurse.
"I must run now."

Thinking It Over

1. When you look back
   on your life so far,
   what was the hardest part?

2. What is your idea
   of a family?

3. What would you do
   if your boss paid you less
   than he or she
   was supposed to?

2 Sticking Together

The next day
Fabian picked up the story
where he had left off.

"I think we should stand up
for better pay!"
Fabian spoke up one day
during his days in Hawaii.

"And better housing!"
added Edmundo.
"These shacks we live in
are worse than what we came from!"

"Don't be so quick,"
said Orlando,
who was head of the *compang*
and older than the others.
"Hundreds of Filipino men
would love to come over here.
The grower will just let us go

and he'll take on those new *Pinoys*.
They will take that low pay.
I say be happy
with what you have.
Besides, you only have
a year left to work."

"A year is a long time,"
said young Fabian Beltran.
"I think we field hands
should go on strike!
Look at us.
There are so many of us now.
The grower couldn't let us all go."

"I think a strike
would be a mistake,"
said Orlando.

But they didn't listen.
Fabian and his friends
began to talk
with the other Pinoys.
They made a plan.
The next Monday morning
when the bell went off,

the young workers
stayed in bed.
When the truck came
to take them to the fields,
they didn't get in.

Orlando was ready for work.
He walked toward the door.
He put one foot out.
Then he stopped,
dead in his tracks.

"What's the matter?"
Fabian asked.
"Go and work if you want."

"I can't,"
said Orlando.
"We are a *compang*.
I am your father.
And this is a strike.
We Pinoys must stick together.
I will stay back
with the rest of you."

The truck outside waited.

"Go on without us!"
Orlando shouted
to the truck driver.
"We are on strike!"

The truck pulled away.
The men waited
to see what would happen.

An hour later
four trucks drove up.
There were men
in the back of each truck.
But these men
were not field hands.
They were police officers.
They had guns,
and they were pointing them
toward the workers' houses.

"Come out now
or we'll shoot!"
they called to the field hands
inside the houses.

No one moved.

Finally, Orlando stepped outside.
"We're on strike!"
he called to the police.
"Tell your friend the grower
we want fair pay
and better housing.
If he says yes
to what we want,
then we will work again."

Fabian watched
as one of the officers
pointed his gun at Orlando.
"He wouldn't shoot anyone,"
Fabian said to himself.
Just then, the gun went off.
Orlando fell to the ground.

Then everything broke open.
Fabian and the rest of his *compang*
ran outside.
So did the workers
from the other houses.
They stormed the trucks
and grabbed at the police.
They shouted and kicked,

and shots rang out all over.
By the time the air cleared,
16 workers and four police officers
lay dead on the ground.
Orlando was one of them.

"I knew I was finished
in Hawaii,"
Fabian told the nurse.
"Not only did we not get
our better pay.
Not only did I see
my *compang* father die for me.
But on top of all this,
we were only treated worse.
We won nothing,
and some people lost their lives."

"So what did you do?"
asked the nurse.

"Well, I finished
my three years in Hawaii,"
said the old man.
"Near the end,
I heard about California.

See, in 1924,
the United States
passed a new law—
the Immigration Act of 1924.
It shut out
the Japanese and Chinese—
all Asians but Filipinos—
from coming into the country.
So the farmers in California
needed cheap labor.
They were happy
to get all us Pinoys.
See, the United States
ruled the Philippines,
so we were U.S. nationals.
So Edmundo and I
moved many more miles
away from our home.
We went to California."

"What happened there?"
asked the nurse.

"Tomorrow,"
said Fabian.
"I'll tell you tomorrow."

Thinking It Over

1. Have you ever been
   in a strike?
   What was it about?

2. What can happen
   when workers
   don't win their strike?

3. For what reasons
   might workers not get
   what they want
   from their strike?

4. Do you think it is fair
   for growers to hire "cheap labor"?
   Why or why not?

3 Life in California

All the Filipino workers
came to California
on their own.
No one paid their way
as they did to Hawaii.
Fabian and Edmundo
joined a group of 15 men
who moved from farm to farm
with the crops.

They worked in the fields
during the spring, summer,
and part of the fall.
During the winter,
Fabian had to find
a different kind of job.

Fabian and Edmundo
got to California

in the spring.
The first work they found
was picking lettuce.
They had to bend over
all day long
in the red-hot sun.
"I found out fast
why they called it 'stoop labor,' "
Fabian told the young nurse.
"When the sun came up,
I was stooped over,
bending down
to pick the lettuce.
And I didn't stop picking
till the sun went down.
I got so hot,
the dust stuck to me
and I itched all the time.
When we worked in the rain,
the mud stuck to our shoes
and made our feet so heavy."

"Where did you live?"
asked the nurse.

"I stayed in a labor camp,"
said Fabian.
"The shacks were dirty and smelly.
All they gave us to eat
was rice and beans and weak coffee.
No vegetables,
even if there were vegetables
rotting out there in the fields.
Every night,
I cried in my bed
from being so tired."

When the lettuce
was all picked,
it was time to move on.
Fabian and Edmundo
headed north to pick grapes.
"That was hard work, too,"
Fabian told the nurse.
"It took a lot of grapes
to fill a basket.
Sometimes it seemed like
a day lasted a whole year."

"But you picked those grapes,"
said the nurse.

"I picked those grapes,"
said Fabian.
"People need their wine!"

"Did you drink some yourself?"
asked the nurse.

"Oh, sure,"
said Fabian.
"On the week-ends
we would go into town
for some fun.
I told you,
we had no Filipino women—
no *Pinays*.
But there were dance halls!"

A picture of the dance hall
came into Fabian's mind.
The sign out front said,
10¢ A DANCE!
The young Pinoys
spent big money
on fancy clothes
to wear to the dance hall
and find a pretty young woman

to dance with,
for one dime after another.

But the women were white.
The law said
that a Filipino man
could not marry
a white American woman.
The dance halls were fun,
but they were not the place
to find a wife.

When the grape season ended,
Fabian went to Stockton
to find a winter job.
Fabian remembered the day
he first went to Stockton.

As he walked down the street,
he felt the eyes
of every white person he passed.
He saw them
passing whispers
as they looked him up and down.

At first Fabian wondered
if there was a hole
in his pants.
He checked himself over.
He found no holes.
Then he knew
what was happening.
People were looking at him
because he was a Pinoy.
No one had to tell him
that these people
did not like his looks.
He knew they hated
the Japanese and Chinese.
But a Filipino?
The Philippines was ruled
by the United States.
That made Fabian
a U.S. national,
with the same rights
as a U.S. citizen.
Why would people
act this way
toward a U.S. national?

None of that mattered
to the people in this town.
"They dance with our women,"
Fabian heard someone whisper.
"They are dirt."

He found a winter job
washing dishes
in a hotel restaurant
without much trouble.
The white people
didn't want such jobs.
The pay was very low,
even for 11 hours a day.
"Take it or leave it,"
said the restaurant owner.
Fabian took it.

However, when Fabian tried
to find a place to live,
it was like talking
to a stone wall.
"You can't live here,"
he was told.
"This is a high-class place."
Fabian watched

as poor old white men
walked in and out
the front door.

   At last he found a room.
It was in an old, run-down hotel.
It was tiny and dirty.
Other Pinoys
lived in the other rooms.

   "There were still no Pinays,"
Fabian told the nurse.
"But there were lots of Pinoys
to have fun with.
And there were dance halls.
Oh, but if only we had
our Filipino women with us.
I know we wouldn't have been
so wild."

Thinking It Over

1. What do you think
   of the law that said
   that Filipino men
   could not marry white women?

2. The Filipinos of this time
   were U.S. "nationals"
   because the United States
   ruled their home Islands.
   Should "nationals"
   have the same rights
   as U.S. citizens?

3. Why do you think
   so few Filipino women
   were in California
   at this time?

4 Bad Feelings

"Your life story
is very interesting,"
the young nurse told Fabian
the next day.

"There's much more to tell!"
said Fabian.
He began his next story.

A few more grape seasons
came and went.
The work was never easy.
And getting along
with the white people
only grew worse.

"I told you that
we couldn't marry white women,"
said Fabian.
"Well, we did make friends
with some dance-hall girls.

I had one girlfriend
I'll never forget.
She was the best-looking
white woman
I ever saw."

"Did you love her?"
asked the nurse.

"Oh, she was more like
someone to have fun with,"
said Fabian.
"We went out together.
I mean,
away from the dance hall.
Oh, the white people went crazy
when they saw us together."

"What did they do?"
the nurse wondered.

"At first,
they just gave us dirty looks,"
said Fabian.
"But over time
things turned really ugly.

Seeing Pinoys with white women
was only the start of it.
The white people said
we were all drunks
and we all broke the law.
Now, you have to remember,
in the 1930s
just about everyone was poor.
So white people started to say
that Filipinos were taking their jobs.
Why, I didn't know a white person
who would want
the kind of work I did!"

    "Did you ever get into a fight
with a white person?"
the nurse asked.

    "Yes, a few times,"
said Fabian.
"White men would come up to me
on the street
and start calling me names.
Sometimes we ended up
pushing each other around.
I gave a few bloody noses

in my day.
I got a few myself, too."

"I guess this happens
when new groups
come into the country,"
said the nurse.

"Oh, but it went far past
a few bloody noses,"
said Fabian.

He told about a very big fight
that broke out at the labor camp.
Some said it started
when a Filipino man
brought a white woman
to the county fair.
Some said it started
when Filipinos threw stones
at a truck driver
who was calling them names.
Then hundreds
of white farm workers
went around to all the camps.
They said they wanted

all the Filipinos off the farms
or they would start fires.
Some of the farms
did tell the Filipinos to leave.
The white people
didn't take the jobs they left anyway.

It was at Fabian's camp
that the big fight broke out.
People threw rocks and bottles.
They beat on each other.
The white people
set fire to some farm buildings
and started shooting guns.
No one forgot that day.

A few months later,
a group of business people
put out a paper.
It said that all Filipinos
were no good
and that they should be
kicked out of the country.
The Filipinos did nothing about this.
But the white people
marched into a dance hall.

They beat up the Filipinos inside.
They broke Edmundo's nose.
They shot at cars
driving by outside.
The fights went on
for the next few days.
Then a crowd of whites
went to one of the farms
and shot into a workers' house.
One Filipino man was killed.

"More and more white people
started talking about
what they called
'the Filipino problem,'"
Fabian went on.
"They decided
they had to fix this problem
once and for all."

"And how did they fix it?"
asked the nurse.

"I'm pretty tired,"
said Fabian.
"I'll tell you more tomorrow."

Thinking It Over

1. Why do bad feelings
   between groups of people
   sometimes get worse
   before they get better?

2. Do you think
   that the Filipinos
   should have been
   made to leave the country?

3. Would you rather
   settle a problem
   by fighting it out
   or talking it out?
   Why?

5 Nationals No More

"So tell me, Fabian,"
said the nurse.
"How did the white Americans
try to fix the 'Filipino problem'?"

"The people here in California
talked to their man in Washington,"
said Fabian.
"One thing led to another.
Then in 1934 they passed a law
that turned us Filipinos
from 'nationals' to 'aliens.'"

"How could they do that?"
the nurse asked.

"Well, the new law
was the first step
for the Philippines
to become its own country,"
said Fabian.

"That was good.
But remember I told you
about the Immigration Act of 1924?
About how the other Asians
were shut out
from coming into the United States?"

"Yes," said the nurse.

"Well, now we Filipinos
came under the same law,"
explained Fabian.
"All of a sudden,
almost no more Filipinos
were coming over here.
Those of us already here
were shut out
of all but the worst jobs—
not that most of us
had good jobs to begin with.
We couldn't get
any of the government services
that were only for Americans.
We also lost our right to vote.
And, of course,
we couldn't expect

any Filipino women
to come over here,
so we couldn't get married."

"Sounds very bad,"
said the nurse.

"It was very bad,"
said Fabian.
"Worst of all,
we were stuck here.
We didn't have enough money
to go back to the Philippines,
and we had no rights
here in the United States."

Fabian told the nurse
about the days after the new law.
The Pinoys felt pretty bad
about how things were going.
They had come to America
to make some money.
While they were growing up
in the Philippines,
they had heard in school
about how well people lived

in America.
Fabian wanted that better life, too.

But here he was,
not well-off at all.
He had come
as a United States national.
Now he was an alien,
with the country
turning against him
and all his friends.

Then more bad news came.
The farm began to let workers go.
One by one,
they were gone.
The Americans were so poor
during the 1930s
that they began to take these jobs.
And since they were citizens
and the Pinoys were not,
the jobs belonged to the Americans.

What's more,
an American who was out of work
could get help

from the government.
Fabian and the other Pinoys
had no place to turn.
He and his friend Edmundo
found a room in Stockton
to live in.
They took any work
they could get.
Most of the time
all they could find
was a yard to clean up
or a wall to whitewash.

A year later,
the U.S. government
came up with a new plan
for the Filipinos in the U.S.

"Have you heard the news?"
said Edmundo,
running into their rented room.
"Word has come down
that the government
will pay our way
back to the Philippines.
It is clear

that we are not welcome here.
What do you say, Fabian?"

"Can't do it,"
Fabian said in a low voice.

"Why not?"
Edmundo wanted to know.

"I came here to make money,"
Fabian began.
"I have to whitewash walls
just to pay the rent.
If I ever go back
to the Philippines,
it will be
with my head held high.
I can't go back
as a poor man."

Both Fabian and Edmundo
stayed in the United States.
Like the Americans
out of work during this time,
they did everything they could
to get back on their feet again.

Thinking It Over

1. Who is your "man
   in Washington"?
   (Hint: It may be a woman,
   and you have
   more than one person
   in Congress.)
   What would you do
   if you wanted these people
   to help you
   or to stand up for you?

2. Are you a U.S. citizen,
   a U.S. national,
   or an alien?
   What does this mean to you?

3. The government did many things
   that hurt the Filipinos
   who came here to work
   back in Fabian's day.
   How do you feel about
   the laws that were passed?

6 Better Times for Hawaii

In 1937,
another law was passed
that hurt most Filipinos in America.
The law said that any aliens
who had signed up
to become U.S. citizens
could take part
in government programs
to help out-of-work people.

"I had come into the country
as a national,"
Fabian told the young nurse.
"I had no reason then
to sign up to be a citizen.
So there was nothing I could do
but ride out the bad times."

"It sounds as if
the government just kept on

hitting you over the head,"
said the nurse.

"You could say that,"
said Fabian.

At last, Fabian and Edmundo
found farm work again.
The pay was very low,
but this was not the time
to ask for more money.
After four months on one farm,
Fabian's group of 15 men
was paid only $50
for all of them.
The farmer had taken out money
to cover their food and housing,
which was worse than ever.
The workers didn't understand
the paper they had signed.
They each ended up with $3.33
for four months of hard work.

One day in the next labor camp,
Fabian picked up a newspaper.
Fabian liked to work out

the English words.
On the front page
he spotted the word *Hawaii.*

"Look at this,"
he said to Edmundo.
"Over in Hawaii
the Filipino farm workers' union
is on strike.
I wish them luck."

Fabian picked up a newspaper
whenever he saw one.
He followed the story
of the farm workers in Hawaii.
Then one day he read good news.

"Edmundo, look!"
Fabian called to his friend.
"They were on strike for 85 days.
That's almost three months!
And listen to this!
They finally won!
They're getting a 15% pay raise!
Oh, I wish I could have been there!
They waited a long time."

"So have we,"
said Edmundo.
"Maybe we should go
back to Hawaii."

"We're stuck here now,"
said Fabian.

"Well, I'm going back to Hawaii
if it takes my last penny,"
said Edmundo.
"It may be hard work,
but I've had enough here.
It's time to move on."

Edmundo returned to Hawaii.
And Fabian lost a friend.
The day Edmundo left California
was the last time
that Fabian saw him
or heard from him.
It was as if he had gone
off the edge of the earth.
But Fabian never forgot Edmundo
and all the hard times
they had shared.

Thinking It Over

1. Have you ever heard
   about something that happened
   to someone else
   that made you very happy?

2. Have you ever had to
   "ride out the bad times"?
   How did you do it?

3. Do you think
   that Edmundo did the right thing
   when he left California
   and returned to Hawaii?
   Why or why not?

4. Is there a person
   you have lost touch with
   from a long time ago?

7 A Family At Last

The nurse shared Fabian's joy
as he told the story
of the workers in Hawaii
getting better pay.
She was sad along with him
to hear about
how Edmundo left California.

"Did you ever wish
you had gone back to Hawaii
to work with the union there?"
asked the nurse.

"No, not really,"
Fabian told her.
"I mean,
I was interested in union work
from my early days in Hawaii.
But during the 1930s and 1940s
I couldn't do much about it
in California."

"Did you ever get to do
any union work?"
asked the nurse.

"Later, much later,"
said Fabian.
"There were unions
in the old days,
but they didn't let
any Pinoys join.
Besides, the farmers in California
didn't believe unions were real
until the 1950s!"

"What did you do
during the 1940s?"
the nurse asked.

"I picked a few million grapes,"
said Fabian.
"And lettuce or beets.
And I went back
to working in a restaurant
during the winter.
But best of all,
I found a wife."

It was 1946.
The Philippines became
a free country.
Filipinos in America
could at last become citizens.
Fabian didn't think much
about becoming a citizen.
What was important to him
was that now,
many young Filipino women
began to come to the U.S.

Fabian was 40 years old
when he met his wife, Patsy.
She kept house
for the farmer and his family
at one of the vineyards
where Fabian worked.
Patsy liked Fabian
as much as he liked her.
But Fabian seemed old to her.
She was only 18.

"I had to work on her,"
Fabian told the nurse.
"But finally she saw things my way,"

he said with a smile.
"She became my wife
and we had four children."

"Were you still going
from crop to crop
after you had children?"
asked the nurse.

"I followed the crops,"
said Fabian.
"And even during grape season,
I moved from farm to farm.
Patsy and our children
stayed on that one farm.
I only saw my family
when I was picking grapes there."

"That is hard,"
said the nurse.

"But I was a happy man
to have a family at last,"
Fabian said.
"That was another thing
I waited a long time for."

Thinking It Over

1. Why do people
   who come to a new country
   become citizens?
   Why might they decide
   not to become citizens?

2. How important is family
   in your life?

3. What would it be like
   to see your family
   only part of the year?

8 The Union Days

Every day,
the young Filipino nurse
looked forward to her visit
with Fabian Beltran.
She drank up Fabian's stories
like a good wine
made from the grapes he picked.

"So you had a family
during the 1950s,"
said the nurse.
"And you worked the fields
all those years?"

"That's right,"
said Fabian.
"I picked vegetables and grapes
all around northern California
for 35 years."

"And then your working days
were over?"
asked the nurse.

"My *picking* days were over,"
said Fabian.
"But not my working days.
I'll tell you how it came about."

When Fabian's children were little,
he and Patsy became citizens.
They felt that they and the children
would be better off that way.

Becoming a citizen
made Fabian feel more important.
He was still a field hand,
but now he felt ready
to stand up for better pay.
Bad as they always were,
the labor camps
and the whole way of working
had only grown worse
over the years.
It was time for farm workers
to be treated better.

During the early 1950s,
Fabian worked with a Pinoy
named Larry Dulay Itliong.
Larry was the one
who got the wheels turning.
"We must work together,"
Larry told Fabian
and the others
each night in the labor camp.
"The big unions
are not interested in us.
So we must start
our own union."

Fabian enjoyed
hearing Larry's talks.
Larry made Fabian
think of himself as a young man
working in Hawaii.
Ever since those days,
Fabian had longed
to start a Filipino union.
He had longed
to help the farm workers.
Larry's was the voice
he wanted to hear.

So in 1956,
Fabian joined Larry
and the other workers
in forming
the Filipino Farm Labor Union.
They called it the FFLU for short.
Right away, the FFLU
started talking with the farmers
about the interests
of the union members.
But the FFLU didn't get very far.
Starting a union
was only the first step.
The next step
was to get the farmers
to see the group as a real union.

Then, before too long,
the new union
opened an important door.
The big union, the AFL–CIO,
voted to stand behind the FFLU.
In 1960 the FFLU
became part of the AFL–CIO.
The FFLU became
the Agricultural Workers

Organizing Committee,
or AWOC for short.

"Someone has to run AWOC,"
Fabian told Larry one day.
"I think it should be you, Larry."
So the union members took a vote.
They made Larry
the head of AWOC.

"I can't do this by myself,"
said Larry.
"We need an office,
and I need a few people
to help me
take care of union business.
Fabian, what do you say?
Will you come and work
for the union?"

At this point,
Fabian was well into his 50s.
All these years of farm work
made him feel old and tired.
But union work
made him feel young again.

"I'd be happy to work for you,"
Fabian said.

"And that is how
I got out of the fields,"
Fabian told the nurse.
"I still went around
and talked to the workers.
I felt like my father Orlando
in the *compang*.
Still, I was one of them.
I *still* am one of them.
I may not be out picking,
but in my heart
I'll always be out there."

"What about the union?"
asked the nurse.
"Did you win better pay
for the members?"

"Now *that's* a story,"
said Fabian.

"I can't wait to hear it,"
said the nurse.

Thinking It Over

1. Have you ever
   been a union member?
   If so,
   how did the union
   work for its members?

2. Did you ever know someone
   who could get people
   all worked up
   the way Larry did?
   Did you follow this person?
   Why or why not?

3. Is your heart
   still in a place
   in which you no longer
   work or live?
   Explain.

9 The Big Strike

"I want to tell you
about the big strike,"
Fabian went on the next day.

"When was this strike?"
asked the nurse.
"What led up to it?"

Fabian remembered
back to the early days of AWOC.
After all these years,
the pay and housing
were still a big problem.
So Fabian and Larry
and the other union workers
went from farm to farm
to talk with the pickers.

"You all know
that the grape season is short,"
Fabian told the pickers.

"If you workers go on strike,
it will mean a big loss
for the farmers.
Grapes would rot on the vine.
A crop could be lost
in just a few weeks."

Grape pickers
at three vineyards
went on strike.
The farmers were upset.
"This strike won't last long,"
Fabian told the pickers.

Fabian was right.
The farmers gave in fast.
The grape pickers
got a pay raise.

More strikes followed.
Fabian helped set up picket lines.
He went from field to field,
talking into a big horn.
"Strike now!"
he shouted.
"You have put up with enough!"

But these strikes
were not quick and clean.
The farmers did not give in.
Larry got another
farm workers' union
to join together in one big strike.
That union was called
the National Farm Workers Union.
Most of its members were Mexican.
It was headed by César Chavez.

The big strike went on and on.
Life got very hard
for the pickers and their families
because they had
no money coming in.

"We have to do something
to help the workers,"
said Fabian's wife, Patsy.
So she and some other women
got people to give clothes and food.
They set up shop
in the town hall.
They made dinners
for the poor workers.

They gave out clothes
for them and their children.

The strike
had no end in sight.
The farmers held fast.
So did the union.

"In 1966,
I was 60 years old,"
Fabian told the nurse.
"But when Larry said,
'We're going to march!'
I said,
'I'm in!'"

"March? March to where?"
asked the nurse.

"We walked to Sacramento,
the state capital,"
said Fabian.

"Wasn't that pretty far
from the fields?"
asked the nurse.

"We walked 230 miles,"
Fabian told her.
"And I didn't get tired,
not even for one mile!
Maybe I was tired
and didn't know it.
I just kept on walking.
There were thousands of people
in the march.
Not all farm workers, either.
Lots of people
felt like us,
that grape pickers
were treated real bad
and didn't get paid enough.
We carried signs
and we shouted
and we made sure
that everyone along the way
knew what we wanted!
We were on TV and everything!"

"Did the march
win your strike for you?"
the nurse asked.

"Believe it or not, no,"
said Fabian.

"You're kidding!"
said the nurse.

"It took another four years,"
said Fabian.

"Another long wait!"
said the nurse.
"And I must wait
until tomorrow
to hear about it."

Thinking It Over

1. Are you old enough to remember
   the great grape strike
   during the 1960s?
   What do you remember about it?

2. Have you ever
   marched or stood up in any way
   for a cause?
   What happened?

3. Have you ever
   given food or clothes
   to people who needed them?

10 The Strike Ends

"After the march,"
Fabian began the next day,
"our AWOC and
the National Farm Workers Union
joined forces.
We became one union—
the United Farm Workers Union.
You've heard of that, right?"

"Yes, I have,"
said the nurse.
"But I think of it
as César Chavez's union."

"Well, that's sort of
how it turned out,"
said Fabian.
"Larry Dulay Itliong
was second under Chavez
in the new union.
But at some point later,

he felt more and more
like a field worker
than a union worker.
So he left the union."

"How about you?
Did you stick around?"
the nurse asked.

"We all stuck out the strike,"
said Fabian.

"So when did it end?"
asked the nurse.
"*How* did it end?"

"My dear young Pinay,
the end of the grape strike
was the best time
of my whole life,"
said Fabian.
"Well, other than when
my children were little!"

He flashed back to 1970.
The grape pickers

had been on strike
for five years.
They didn't give up.
There were people
walking the picket lines
at dozens of vineyards.
They were out there every day
as if the strike
had just started the day before.
And Fabian still went
from farm to farm
to help them keep up their fight.

The people of America
were behind the grape pickers.
Many people stopped buying grapes
and California wines.
The farmers were in trouble.
They had lost their good workers
and millions of dollars in sales, too.

Then one day
Fabian was sitting
in the union office.
The phone rang
and he picked it up.

It was Larry.
"It's over,"
came Larry's voice.
"Two vineyards signed papers today.
The workers are back on the job.
They'll get higher pay
and the farmers
will fix up the labor camps."

"That's great!"
said Fabian.
"But what are the other vineyards
going to do?"

"They'll fall in line,"
said Larry.
"It's just a matter of time."
Soon the other vineyards
signed the papers.
So did the nut growers.
At last,
life would get a little better
for farm workers.

Fabian went around
to all the vineyards

to talk to the workers.
He also went to make sure
the farmers carried out
what they said they would do.

   "I waited 48 years
to see this day!"
Fabian told the workers
in the vineyards.
"Now you Pinoys
keep up the good work.
Maybe you can even work yourself
off the farms and into better jobs.
I know some of your
uncles and cousins
have done that already.
And don't any one of you forget
all the pain and years
that went into your fight.
You have won a great war,
not only for yourselves
but for those who come after you.
You are strong, strong people,
my Pinoy family.
Never forget
there is power in your hands."

There were tears
in the nurse's eyes.
She took Fabian's hand.
It was hard like a rock
and rough like sandpaper.
It was a strong hand,
even if it was old.

"And that was the end
of my working days,"
said Fabian.

"I've enjoyed
hearing your story,"
said the nurse.

"I've enjoyed telling it,"
laughed Fabian.
"I wish more people cared."

"Everyone should know
the great work
you and your people did,"
said the nurse.
"You helped make fair fields!"

Thinking It Over

1. Do you think
   you could ever feel
   strongly enough about something
   to stay on strike
   for five years?

2. What do you think
   would happen today
   if a union stayed on strike
   as long as the farm workers did?

3. Do you think
   that the people
   who came before you
   helped make your life better?
   How did they do this?

4. What do you think
   the nurse means
   by "fair fields"?

11 The Filipino Nurse

"And what about you?"
asked Fabian.
"I've been talking away
for days now,
and I still
don't even know your name.
I guess I was
so busy talking
I never got around
to asking your name."

"It's right here
on my name tag,"
said the nurse.

"Oh, sure enough,"
said Fabian.
"You read it to me.
My eyes aren't so good
these days."

"My name is Trini Rizal,"
said the nurse.

"Is that so?"
said Fabian.
"José Rizal was the name
of a very great Filipino man.
He wrote a famous book
against Spanish rule of the Islands.
It set off a war.
It changed everything.
And Rizal was the last name
of my old friend Edmundo.
Now what do you think of that?"

"I wondered
when we would get to my name,"
smiled Trini, the nurse.
"I have something to tell you.
Edmundo Rizal was my father.
As your story moved along,
I put it all together."

"What?" said Fabian.
He couldn't believe his ears.

"As a very young man,
my father went to Hawaii,
then to California,
then back to Hawaii,"
Trini explained.
"He got hurt very badly
cutting sugar cane,
so he returned to the Philippines.
He married my mother,
and I am their third and last child.
My father died
a few years after I was born.
Other than these facts,
I never knew much
about my father
until I heard your story."

For a minute,
Fabian couldn't find words
to say all that he felt.
Then he reached
for the nurse's hand
and said,
"Trini Rizal,
I loved you
from the first day

you came in here
to give me my shot!
Edmundo Rizal
was like a brother to me.
And you are like a daughter.
Now, tell me,
why did *you* come to America?"

"I am a nurse,"
said Trini.
"I came a long way
back in the Philippines
to become a nurse.
But the fact is,
I can make
ten times as much money here
as I could back there.
I came here to help my family
and to build a better life
for myself.
Things are very crazy
back in the Philippines
with President Marcos
and his wife.
It's only going to get worse.
I'm much better off here."

"You have a story, too,"
said Fabian.
"Say, are you married?"

"Still looking!"
Trini laughed.
"Do you know
any nice young men?"

"Well, I have a son
who's not married yet,"
said Fabian.
"Want to meet him?"

"Maybe," said Trini
with a smile.
"Now it's time for your shot.
Let's try your left arm today."

Just then,
a woman walked
into the hospital room.

"Patsy!" said Fabian.
"Trini Rizal,

this is my dear wife, Patsy.
Patsy, meet Edmundo's daughter.
You remember me
talking about my long-lost friend
all these years.
And now his daughter
pops up out of the blue.
Isn't it a small world?"

Thinking It Over

1. Have you ever said,
   "It's a small world"?
   What were you talking about
   when you said that?

2. Did you ever know anyone
   who seemed to "pop up
   out of the blue"?
   What does this mean?

3. Would you be willing
   to move to a new place
   in hopes of a better life,
   as both Fabian and Trini did?
   Why or why not?